Diana Hunt.

April 1981.
G.H.

First published in Great Britain 1980
by Tabb House, 11 Church Street, Padstow,
Cornwall.

ISBN 0 907018 03 3

Printed in Great Britain
by
Tanhoit Ltd, St. Austell, Cornwall.

POLLACK AND CARNIVAL

Cornish Stories

by

Walter Walkham

TABB HOUSE

Padstow, Cornwall
1980

Contents

THE LAWN MEET

YOU drive right past Chy Vean on the road to Land's End. You probably wouldn't even notice it.

When Jill and I were children, it was a very different place, standing behind a wide, well-kept lawn. Today, however, it still has the home farm buildings at the back and rolling pastures all round.

Great-grandpa Williams lived there all his life. The villagers called him Cap'n Sam, though he was never captain of anything except his own household.

In Great-grandpa's day, Chy Vean was a magic place, with all sorts of creatures and other advantages we couldn't have at home, like pony-rides, domestic servants and trees to climb.

You entered the house through a conservatory where you ran the gauntlet of hundreds of powerfully-smelling, potted geraniums. Then you turned left into a gloomy hall, its walls cluttered with trophies and sporting prints. There were fox masks and brushes galore, various stuffed birds and other heirlooms, including a silver cup since handed down to Mother: some manure manufacturers in Penzance had awarded it to Great-grandfather in the 1880's for the best field of mangolds grown with their product.

The hall smelt permanently of cooking, especially of cabbage, despite the green baize door which separated the kitchen area. When you went into the drawing-room, the vegetable smell changed to animal; Great-aunt Alice, Great-grandpa's maiden daughter, kept her Jack Russell terriers in there, with their putrid dog-beds in every corner.

The drawing-room walls were crowded with oil paintings of horses and hounds and prize-winning bullocks, relieved by a portrait of our late Great-grandma in the place of honour over the mantelpiece. The fire was lit daily, even at midsummer, and facing it stood a high-backed chair, the focal point of the household, to be approached only with reverence and circumspection.

You had to walk round the chair to pay homage to Great-grandpa. Jill and I learned early to keep clear of Great-grandpa's stick, until summoned for conversation.

The master of Chy Vean was an awesome sight, with gimlet eyes in a long, livid face, and a dewlap which wobbled when he spoke. His hoarse, staccato voice was not unlike the baying of foxhounds. For emphasis, he banged the floor with his stick.

Jill used to say Great-grandpa stank as much as the terriers; she probably exaggerated. But neither of us engaged Great-grandpa in conversation longer or more frequently than politeness required, and it was always a relief to withdraw in good order from his piercing glare and gruff manner.

Dinner at Chy Vean was taken in the early afternoon. Great-grandpa dominated the ceremony; there was no escape. He ate slowly, and his meal seemed to go on for ever. Long after everyone else had finished, the master's cheese was brought to him, and the dish cover removed. The effluvium soon pervaded the whole dining-room; even today I stop breathing when I think of it.

One day after dinner I overheard Mother telling Grannie, "I'll swear I saw Grandpa's cheese move on the dish."

After that, Jill and I used to study the cheese minutely for locomotion, and I remember a nightmare in which the cheese, crawling with maggots, heaved itself off the dish and marched across the tablecloth to assault me.

Our distaste was not lost on Great-grandpa. He once stared us each out of countenance and growled, "Look pleasant, can't you?"

Great-grandpa employed a manservant called Northey. In retrospect, I think Northey must have been an idle rogue, though he knew how to please us children, and he seemed to suit Great-grandpa well enough. Each morning during the hunting season, he had to groom and saddle Great-grandpa's hunter, Duke, and parade him on the lawn outside the drawing-room French windows. I couldn't remember Great-grandpa ever electing to go hunting, or even hacking for years on end, but he insisted on his horse being ready, in case he decided to ride out.

Once during the Christmas holidays, while Chy Vean was still enchanted, Great-aunt Alice invited the master of the foxhounds to call a meet on the lawn. The occasion was Great-grandpa's eighty-sixth birthday, and the older hunt members promised a numerous gathering to honour their former master.

You can imagine the excitement at Chy Vean as the family prepared to play host to the hunt, a role new to Jill and me. Mother went into Penzance and bought dozens of sherry glasses for the stirrup-cup, so that we wouldn't have to use the chipped glasses in the dining-room sideboard. Northey spent a whole day cleaning the windows in the front of the house. Grannie organised the maid in a dawn-to-dusk cleaning of the hall and staircase, in case any of the ladies needed to come inside the house; she also sprayed the place in an unsuccessful attempt to kill the cabbage smell. There was even talk of moving the Jack Russells out of the drawing-room, but Great-aunt Alice drew the line at that.

On his birthday, Great-grandpa came downstairs an hour earlier than usual. He astonished us all by appearing in his hunting breeches and pink coat, which added a camphoric smell to the other Chy Vean odours.

"Send Northey with my boots," croaked Great-grandpa, brandishing his stick and hobbling to the drawing-room, where the fire hadn't yet been lit.

Northey, probably caught still shaving or breakfasting, pushed through the baize door at long last, wiping the mildew off Great-grandpa's riding boots.

"Is Master going hunting sure enough?" he asked us children in astonishment.

I hovered at the drawing-room door while Northey assisted a growling, cantankerous master into his boots.

Presently the old gentlemen bawled, "Send my

great-grandson here!"

In trepidation I went to Great-grandpa and wished him many happy returns of the day.

"Humph!" he snorted. "You'll ride the pony today. Your Great-aunt Alice will fit you up with the gear. Understand? Here's your cap money."

Breathless with excitement, I squeaked, "Thank you, Great-grandpa!" and took the half-crown he held out to me.

"Humph!" he growled, raising his stick. "Mind you don't get in anyone's way. Understand?"

"Yes, Great-grandpa," I breathed and retired swifly, to harass Great-aunt Alice for the riding clothes.

Great-aunt tut-tutted, because she had enough to worry about already, but she found me some moth-eaten jodhpurs (for feminine wear, without fly buttons, though I didn't notice it at the time) and an elderly hard hat that I had to support with my ears.

I strutted about, slapping my legs with a riding crop, to emphasise my new status. This annoyed poor Jill, because she was going to be left out of the hunt, but Mother partially consoled her by dressing her up to carry a salver with the stirrup-cup.

Meanwhile, Grannie and Great-aunt Alice remonstrated with Great-grandpa about the dangers of hunting at his time of life, until he drove them out of the drawing-room at the end of his stick. Northey paced the lawn with Duke, muttering, "Master never oughta do it!" And so the time passed, until the hunt started to assemble on the lawn.

Great-grandpa tottered outside to greet his guests, some of whom he hadn't seen for years. About three dozen riders turned up − a large field indeed for those days, when few people owned horse-boxes. All, from the master to the youngest farmer's son, made a gratifying fuss of Mr Williams, or Cap'n Sam, as they variously called him. The lawn filled with riders, horses, hounds and followers, and Great-grandpa's normally fierce expression softened to eager anticipation.

Presently the huntsman toot-tooted his horn and, fortified with sherry, we mounted. Great-grandpa used the granite mounting block, roundly cursing Northey, without whose help he would never have got his leg across Duke. The pony, Smokey, with me astride, was led alongside Duke and Great-grandpa, to be photographed for the *Cornishman* newspaper.

We moved off at a trot, taking the hounds across the twelve-acre field below the lawn, to draw Trenoweth Bottom. Smokey and I kept company in the rear, among the youngsters detailed to close gates. Ahead of us at the bottom end of Twelve-acre, a couple of the more dashing members of the field ignored the gateway and took the bank with a jump on and off.

Following in Great-grandpa's tracks, I saw Duke break into a canter, heading for the bank.

"Cap'n Sam!" shouted one of the young farmers. "Put him through the gate!"

"Keep clear!" bawled Great-grandpa, standing in his stirrups.

We watched fascinated as Duke rose to the bank, stumbled on top of it and disappeared on the far side. When the horse regained his feet, we could see that the saddle was empty.

"Aw, my dear days!" exclaimed the young farmer who'd tried to persuade Great-grandpa through the open gateway.

I wasn't worried at first, thinking Great-grandpa was indestructible. Then, in the next field, we found him lying quite still in the brambles. He looked so small and frail, especially with Duke standing over and nuzzling him; Duke's head was nearly as big as his owner's body. I knew that Great-grandpa had ridden to hounds for the last time.

The young farmers took the gate off its hinges for a stretcher, and laid Cap'n sam on it. Then we headed back in solemn procession to the house, I leading Smokey and Duke, the latter very lame in the near fore. No-one spoke.

Northey came out and relieved me of Duke and Smokey. As the stretcher party entered the conservatory, the hunting horn sounded in the distance.

Through the geraniums we went, and through the boiled cabbage to the staircase, the Jack Russells yapping their protest at the intrusion. Guilded by Great-aunt Alice, the farmers carried Great-grandpa upstairs and gently transferred him from the gate to his bed.

Great-grandpa made neither sound nor movement. While we waited for Dr Sykes to arrive, Great-aunt Alice went round the house, drawing all the curtains.

Dr Sykes called three times that day. Before he left in the evening, I heard him tell Great-aunt Alice, "His heart's still beating — just, But you must be prepared for the worst, Miss Williams. I'll call again in the morning."

When I went upstairs to bed, I heard sobbing in Great-grandpa's room. The door was ajar and I tiptoed towards it.

In the glimmer of the nightlight, I saw Northey kneeling, his body heaving and his cheeks wet with tears. I didn't know grown men behaved like that.

Presently, as Northey buried his face in his hands, I saw Great-grandpa's frame curl, ever so slowly, on the bed. Then suddenly he sat up, his dewlap quivering.

"Northey!" he croaked.

"A — ah!" gasped Northey, falling off his knees on to his buttocks.

Great-grandpa raised an accusing finger and demanded, "Have you got the vet for Duke's leg yet?"

Duke lived another ten lazy winters after that, and died aged thirty. Northey found him stiff on the stable floor one morning. The previous day, he'd paraded Duke outside the French windows as usual.

Great-grandpa Williams died three days after his horse, aged ninety-six.

Chy Vean? The lawn is a licensed caravan park now, and the house itself a bed-and-breakfast place. I often wonder if the hall still smells of boiled cabbage.

THE WAGES OF SIN

THEY used to say, "There's three kinds of people in Cornwall: good, bad and Laity." But you had to be careful about repeating it, and even today you must'nt let Willie Pascoe hear you.

Farmer Harold Laity was once chairman of the magistrates down here; they still tell the story about the time Mark Tonkin, one of his hands, was brought up before him on a drunk and disorderly charge.

Asked if he had anything to say, Mark spluttered, "I weren't drunk, Mr Harold. You saw me. You was there. Why, you bought me a drink! Just after closing time, it was, and . . ."

"Hrrrmph!" Farmer Laity interrupted him. "Fined ten shillings."

Still protesting, Mark Tonkin was led away, while his master handed the clerk a ten-shilling note and called, "Next case."

Ah! Justice was swift in those days, and left few scars. What were we talking about? Oh, yes, Willie Pascoe. He was a boy then, when beer was only fivepence a pint, and he was too young to appreciate it. He preferred pop at a penny a bottle, with a half-penny back on the bottle.

The local bobby was a silly man from somewhere Launceston way, and when Willie sauced him, he found himself summonsed for riding his push-bike at night without lights, brakes, bell, anything except a frame and wheels. Of course, he came up before young Farmer Laity, who was an awesome enough man for a boy to face. He gave Willie a lecture about the terible result of a life of crime, and then let him off with a caution.

Like any other boy, Willie was partial to apples, especially the sweeter kind you don't buy. When he and Simon Trembath saw Farmer Laity's ripe russets and Laxtons hanging in the orchard across the meadow, you can imagine the effect on them.

Willie should have remembered his police court lecture, but it didn't take him long to cross the meadow, keeping close to the hedge for concealment. Simon Trembath went along, too, sharing Willie's nerve, because he hadn't got so much of his own. Willie peered over the orchard hedge and, finding the coast clear, led the way over. Soon they were treading on apples: bruised, scarred, worm-eaten, rotten ones. The good ones were still on the trees and Willie deftly picked those he could reach, stowing them inside his shirt. The best apples were higher up and Willie climbed for them, weighing the branches down for Simon to reach. It did'nt take long to collect as many as they could carry away between them.

Then they heard a man's voice talking quietly, and they saw a man leaning on the orchard gate. Both boys froze, Willie in the tree and Simon below it. The tree gradually stopped swaying, until it was as still as its neighbours. The man stood staring over the gate — straight at them, perhaps. He was the first to move; he partly opened the gate.

Willie and Simon prayed, harder then they had ever done in chapel, and put their trust in absolute immobility. But not for long. Bounding towards them came a bull terrier, panting for action. Simon shot up the tree like a squirrel, shedding apples as he climbed.

The dog gazed up at them, his huge jaws open with great ribbons of saliva hanging from them. The boys could see right down his throat. They couldn't have been more impressed by a crocodile.

Nobody came near them for a long time. The bull terrier lay down, but he was alert; when Willie tried to come down from his perch, the dog lifted his head and displayed his jaws again, so Willie decided he would stay in the tree a little longer.

Presently Farmer Laity came into the orchard and walked straight up to their tree, stooping to fasten a chain on the dog's collar. Without looking up, he said, "Right, you boys, you can come down now."

Meekly, the boys descended and stood facing the chairman of the magistrates.

"Hah! You again!" said Farmer Laity. "William John Pascoe, did you come by bicycle?"

"N-no, sir," replied Willie, "we walked here."

"Now you can walk up to the house," said Farmer Laity, pointing to the gate.

Willie went in front, followed by Simon and then Farmer Laity with the bull terrier. No-one spoke and Willie couldn't help thinking of the preacher banging the pulpit in chapel and shouting, "Brethren, the wages of sin is death!" If only Willie had paid more heed!

He stopped at the back door, trembling with anxiety. Farmer Laity fastened the bull terrier and solemnly beckoned the boys to follow him into the kitchen.

"You're a funny shape," observed Farmer Laity, prodding the boys' shirts where the apples bulged.

Sheepishly, Willie and Simon unloaded the apples, placing them on the long, scrubbed kitchen table.

"You look a lot thinner now," said the magistrate. "My word, you are thin boys. Sit down there ... Laura, I want a word with you."

The woman at the stove straightened her apron and followed Farmer Laity into the hall, while the boys sat stiffly at the end of the table. They could hear the voices in the hall, but not clearly enough to learn their fate. Presently the woman returned, removing the apples from the kitchen table in a basket. She glanced at the boys, her lips pursed with disapproval.

Willie plucked up the courage to ask, "What's going to happen, Mrs. Pender?"

"You just sit there," snapped Laura Pender, "and do exactly what you'm told. Master'll decide what to do with you when he's had his dinner."

There was a lovely smell of dinner in the kitchen, but the boys had been too scared to notice it. They couldn't help noticing the dinner when it came out of the oven: steak and kidney pudding it was, with boiled potatoes, carrots and cabbage. Laura carried it all and the hot dinner plates on a tray to the dining-room. When she returned, she had three plates of dinner on the tray and she placed two of them in front of the boys.

"There," she said. "Get that inside you. It may be the last you'll have for a while."

"D'you mean," asked Willie, "we're going to prison?"

"I dunno," admitted Laura, "but I expect you deserve it. Just keep quiet and behave yourselves, and I don't suppose no harm will come to you — much."

At these comforting words, Willie and Simon dug into the steak and kidney pudding — and the apple pie and cream which followed, though they were flagging before the end. They'd hardly finished their mugs of tea when Farmer Laity re-appeared, and they stood up.

"You boys still hungry?" he demanded.

"No, sir," said Willie.

"Well, listen," said the magistrate. "If you ever want anything from me, you just step right up and ask me. You don't have to come sneaking around to take it while I'm not looking. Will you remember that?"

"Yes, sir," gasped Willie. "Thank you, sir."

"Right," said Farmer Laity. "Now you cut along."

The boys needed no second bidding. In the twinkling of an eye, they were out of the kitchen, past the bull terrier and half way back to the village.

It was the only time Simon Trembath was in any kind of trouble. Willie, too, was a reformed character — as far as Farmer Laity's apples were concerned. He always scrobbed them from someone else afterwards. And to this day he won't hear a bad word spoken of a Laity.

POLLACK AND CARNIVAL

"MACKEREL! Four a penny, mackerel!"

How long would you have to turn the clock back, to hear that cry in the streets of Penzance? A hundred years? Two hundred?

No; only to the thirties, to the days when I spent school summer holidays there. Mind you, mackerel were only as cheap as this in a glut, and even then the price went up in Morrab Road. How do I know? Well, I wasn't an ordinary visitor, for just a week or a fortnight. I had cousins in Penzance, so I belonged. That's why I could go to the fish-packing station at Newlyn and buy a crab for sixpence: a crab that was only slightly undersized or had a deformed claw.

Crab was a luxury. So were mackerel from a street barrow. We preferred to catch our own sea-food, from the Penzance pierhead. Pollack were the best: anything from twelve ounces upwards. Tiddlers we returned to the sea, and also pouting (we called them 'footballers' for their striped backs) and the brightly-clad wrasse (I don't know why we called them 'rock bass') which were too bony for eating. Pollack were the thing: streamlined, green-backed, golden-flanked, silver-bellied pollack, fried and eaten with two penn'orth of chips from the Adelaide chip shop.

One pollack became quite a celebrity for a week or two. He was big for an inshore fish, about four pounds, and he made a tour of inspection of the pierhead every evening an hour before sunset, scorning all bait. He was distinguished by a livid gash on the starboard flank, said to have been inflicted by the propeller screw of the R.M.S. *Scillonian* while she berthed alongside. (I mean the first *Scillonian;* the ship at present in service is the third of that name.)

My rod was typical, and it cost tenpence halfpenny: sixpence for a light bamboo pole and fourpence for eyes, line, trace and hooks. For a sinker, I used a flint, pierced by the elements and found on Eastern Green beach. Floats we considered unnecessary. We also managed without reels by 'whiffing', gathering the line with the fingers of one hand, to keep the bait moving. Our prowess used to amaze the 'visitors,' who came to the pierhead with their expensive greenheart rods and got scarcely a bite—until one of use took pity and sold them the secret.

The secret was the bait. Fussy, soft-mouthed Mr Pollack was attracted only to the lugworm, known in foreign parts as the ragworm. Lugs were to be had at low water in the huge small-boat harbour, now largely filled for a car park. The best spot was close to the gasworks, where the sewers discharged. Here the silt was blackest and lugs were most abundant. You could get a tobacco-tin full in an hour's digging before the tide returned.

Shameful prices we used to charge the 'visitors' for lugs, but to charge less would have spoilt the trade for everyone. And the proceeds we needed to keep us, not only in chipped potatoes, but in cinema as well. We patronised the Picturedrome, which stood between the *Cornishman* newspaper office and the top entrance to Morrab Gardens. A seat cost fourpence, and the programme changed every Monday and Thursday. Charlie Chan was our favourite performer.

The highlight of every summer was undoubtly Carnival Week, when even the pollack were relegated to secondary importance. Everyone who belonged caught the carnival spirit, and most people belonged in those days, before Woolworths arrived in Market Jew Street and heralded an invasion of big, foreign traders.

The old family traders organised a What's Wrong with this Window? competition, and you had to discover and write down on a form the deliberate mistakes in the window displays of scores of shops. Some shops ran their own competitions, like guessing the number of seeds in a bowl. The prize for that was a caged dove, and how we envied the young chap from Heamoor who won him!

The most important competition was for the title of Carnival Queen; this was decided by popular vote. Photographs of the competitors wer displayed at strategic points in the town, and voting tickets sold at a penny each. The tallies were recorded daily on vertical scales like great thermometers on the Promenade.

One year there were four contestants, of whom two easily outstripped their rivals: Ida George, who lived down in the harbour area, drawing steadily ahead of Miss Bartlett from Morrab Road. Being quite sure that Ida was the prettiest girl in Penzance, we were dismayed when Miss Bartlett leapt into the lead the day before the crowning cermony.

Uproar followed. It was obvious that the well-to-do residents of Morrab Road had bought block tickets for Miss Bartlett, their wealth out-bidding justice and circumventing the democratic process. Such underhanded behaviour could not go unchallenged, and the subsequent protest meeting was well attended by Ida's supporters, the press and the police.

By a stroke of genius, the carnival committee crowned two queens that year, and ordered a second carriage. The master-stroke, though, was the decision that Ida's carriage would precede Miss Bartlett's in the procession the following day.

Carnival Day dawned bright and clear. Not until the London papers arrived did we realise that our carnival, with dual queens, was front-page news. The supercilious London editors treated the whole episode in light, even hilarious vein. But it was no laughing matter, I can tell you, for those who belonged.

In the early evening, the carnival crowded the Recreation Field for judging. The decorated float section was won, not for the first time, by Doctor Penny of Marazion. This year he showed a galleon, manned by a swarm of enthusiastic, diminutive pirates. At last the stewards got the procession under way, Penzance Silver Band leading. Then followed the queens in horse-drawn landaus, the decorated floats, the equestrian and finally the pedestrian entries. We watched them all go past: Red Indians, chocolate soldiers, Britannias, columbines, Queen Elizabeths (the First, of course), Puss in Boots, the lot. Then we raced down to the harbour for a good spot to see it all again.

Cornwall Constabulary attended in force at the harbourside. As the strains of the band swelled, the atmosphere tightened. The radiant heroine, Ida George, received a rapturous welcome from her neighbours, the womenfolk especially shrieking their approval. But how quickly their joy changed to fury, when Miss Bartlett's carriage passed!

Poor Miss Bartlett! Pale and erect, she drove like Marie Antoinette to the scaffold through a torrent of garbage and abuse. I burned with shame as a cabbage-stalk sailed through the air and struck her shoulder. Suddenly I wanted to jump into her carriage and hurl the rubbish back at the crowd, but the wall of blue-serged policemen was impenetrable. And then the queens had gone, and the pirates of Penzance were firing confetti at us through their gun-ports. It was an ordinary carnival again, though my faith in human nature had been shaken for ever.

The carnival over, we returned to the pollack and Charlie Chan. September came all too soon, and school. But at least we who belonged could look forward to the next summer of pollack and carnival.

VISITORS

"I'LL be glad when they've all gone home."

The neighbouring women used to tell Alan's mother this, over the back garden wall. But if they meant it, why did they take in summer visitors, like Alan's mother?

Without the visitors, Alan didn't suppose there'd be any carnival, regatta, summer theatre, beach sports, ice cream or even any fine weather, because all these things disappeared when the visitors left Newquay at the end of the season.

You never knew what your next visitors were going to be like, until they arrived. Except the Kesseners, who came every year. They were quite old. They had a grand Armstrong-Siddeley motor-car, and they used to take Alan all over Cornwall in it.

They didn't just go to nearby places like Holywell and Bedruthen Steps, but places a long way off like St. Ives, Penzance, Falmouth and Fowey. They used to stuff Alan with food and when they got home in time for dinner (which everyone else in the street called 'tea' and ate an hour earlier) Mr Kessener used to recall everything Alan had eaten since breakfast.

"He's had a pasty, some egg and tomato sandwiches, four bottles of pop, a fish and chip lunch, four ice creams, a cream tea, two bars of chocolate and a quarter pound of toffees."

Alan's mother said the Kesseners were kind to him because they hadn't any children of their own. But other visitors were kind to him, too, and some of them had children.

Not the Smiths. Never the Smiths. It was remarkable how many Smiths they had among their visitors. They were always young people, who had no children. The Smiths were late risers, and too absorbed in each other to notice anyone else.

The most interesting visitors were other children. Some of them were soft, and dominated by their parents; some got nasty if their parents even noticed Alan; some thought they they owned Alan's house and things. Others were all right, and you could go swimming and fishing and rock climbing though the girls were a drag sometimes.

One year everything seemed different. The Kesseners didn't come, for one thing. Also, Alan had lost interest in swimming and fishing rock pools and scaling cliffs. And he'd lost interest in the visiting children who wanted to do these things.

At the time, Alan was in love with Janet Gaynor, star of the silver screen, darling of the talking pictures. He used to play a record of her singing 'If I had a Talking Picture of You' over and over again on his mother's gramaphone, while he conjured up the pretty, wide-eyed features he'd seen at the cinema. He wondered if Janet Gaynor was responsible for his changing taste in entertainment.

Something else changed that summer: they had only one pair of Smiths and, more remarkably, they were not a young couple, but a mother and daughter. The daughter was said to be of Alan's age, and he wondered idly if she would be anything like Janet Gaynor.

Sally Smith proved to be nothing like Janet Gaynor, but she easily made up for that. She had a round face with freckles, bright blue eyes and ginger hair. Most importantly, she was right there in Newquay, and when she smiled, it wasn't for the cinema-going public; it was for Alan. Sally was a real, colourful, three-dimensional girl, not a flat, shadowy image. Alan forgot all about Janet Gaynor.

Poor Mrs Smith didn't have much of a holiday. She saw Sally only at meal times; otherwise, Sally spent the whole week with Alan, and they didn't want anyone else.

Alan recovered his zest for bathing. When Sally tucked her hair into a rubber bathing cap, she looked quite grown-up. Alan proudly accompanied her waist-deep into the sea. She let

Alan try to teach her to swim breaststroke, his arms supporting her bumpy, white body while she thrashed her limbs about. The exercise made Sally gasp and giggle, and it made Alan tingle with a new and fascinating sensation.

"Don't let me go!" shrieked Sally, though it was the last thing Alan wanted to do.

After the swimming lesson, they couldn't get close enough to each other, or far enough away from other people. They went everywhere leaning on each other, their hot, sticky fingers intertwined. They sat together for hours on end, exchanging confidences.

Sally told Alan all about herself. Mrs Smith wasn't her natural mother, but had adopted her as a baby. Her real name was Winston-Burnett, with a hyphen. The Winston-Burnetts, she said, were a very posh family, who had a country seat in the North of England and a private park with horses and peacocks and a footman to serve breakfast in bed. When she was twenty-one, she would come into some money and jewellery, though she would have to make her own way in the world. Meanwhile, Sally had to live with Mrs Smith in a dingy street in a dreary neighbourhood.

Alan couldn't match Sally for romanticism, and he could hardly believe his good fortune in having as his first and last lover a girl of such beauty, grace and aristocratic descent.

Dreaded Saturday came, when Mrs Smith took Sally home. At the railway station, in front of a platform full of people, Sally kissed Alan passionately on the lips to sweeten the sorrow of parting.

As soon as Sally's train had disappeared, Alan went straight home and wrote to her at the Durnford Street, Stonehouse, Plymouth address which Mrs Smith had given.

He wrote every day at first. But no reply ever came. Alan stopped writing, and eventually he stopped even looking for a letter from Plymouth in the morning post.

Gradually the wound healed, and Alan became aware of other girls: quieter, more reserved girls, who took the trouble to answer letters. But they weren't as exciting as Sally.

Durnford Street went out of Alan's mind for several years, but Sally didn't. Then the war came and Alan joined the Royal Marines. He first reported to the RM Barracks at Stonehouse. Some days later, when Alan learned that the street alongside the barracks was called Durnford Street, he recalled the number of Mrs Smith's house.

One evening, clad in his newly-issued battle dress, he went inquiring for Sally. He found the house, and climbed the short flight of steps to ring the doorbell. There were several bell-buttons, all labelled but none with the name of Smith. Alan selected the bottom button and pressed it.

A young woman opened the door; she had auburn hair framing a round, lacquered face, and her bright blue eyes had crowsfeet at the corners.

"Sally Smith," breathed Alan.

"I'm Sally Johnson now," she corrected him. "Who are you?"

"Alan . . . Don't you remember? Newquay?"

"Oh, yes!" exclaimed Sally, smiling now. "That was a long time ago. Come in."

Alan followed her down to the basement and into an ill-lit room. A baby was in a corner and Sally picked it up. A toddler came out of the gloom to investigate the visitor.

"How's Mrs Smith?" asked Alan.

"Mother died," said Sally. "I've let all the upstairs rooms. I've got plenty of room down here, especially while my husband's at sea."

Alan felt like a trespasser. He declined tea, lying about an appointment he had to keep. After he'd admired the children, Sally let him escape. At the front door, they shook hands with a strange feeling of contentment.

Alan descended the steps to street level. Then he turned and asked, "By the way, did you ever learn the breaststroke?"

"I could swim," boasted Sally, "years before I met you." She waved and, still smiling, closed the door.

THE FORESHEETHAND

BRITANNIA, Shamrock V, Astra, Candida: the great J Class yachts were coming to Plymouth for the regatta. Richard had some of them in his 'Yachts and Motor Boats' cigarette card set (a series of 50 issued by Ogden's Tobacco). And now Commander Jones had invited him to sail down to Plymouth to see the big yachts racing in the Sound!

Commander Jones, RN (retired) was Richard's neighbour in Lower Port View, Saltash. He kept a boat down on the wharf and spent much of his time painting it or otherwise caring for it, besides providing professional advice to all boat owners. Occasionally he took someone — a different person each time — out for a sail on the river. Richard thought there was no limit to his kindness, until he sailed with him.

As soon as they were afloat, Commander Jones' nature changed completely. He barked orders as though he were aboard a windjammer in a Cape Horn gale, instead of merely instructing the foresheethand alongside him in a sixteen-foot sailing boat. And he used a strange vocabulary, so that Richard didn't know what to make of such orders as, 'Belay foresheet,' 'Lower the centreboard,' and 'Trim the dish.'

The only thing that looked to Richard remotely like a dish was the baler, so he picked it up and handed it to Commander Jones. His reward was to be called a bloody fool.

Most of the passage from Saltash to Plymouth Sound they spent perched in wet trousers on one side of the boat with the other side partly buried in the water, while Richard wondered how soon the lower side would go just a little lower and let the River Tamar in. Gradually, though, Richard learnt what his skipper meant by 'going about,' and how it was done, and what 'port' and 'starboard,' 'tack,' 'weather side' and 'lee side' meant, and that the sheets weren't the sails, but the ropes you controlled them with. He also learnt why nobody ever sailed with Commander Jones twice.

By the time they were well down the Hamoaze among the warships, Richard's confidence had so recovered that he was able to look about him, observing the vessels they passed and even waving to the passengers on the Torpoint ferry, which gesture Commander Jones condemned as a breach of discipline. Then the sun came through the clouds and the wind eased until the fierce ebb tide was doing as much as the sails to carry them into the Sound. The boat sailed on her bottom instead of her side, and Richard and Commander Jones could sit inside her and eat their sandwiches.

Drake's Island came in sight, and the Sound beyond, with the white sails of yachts all over it. The water sparkled in the warm sun and a moderate breeze gave perfect sailing. Out to sea were the big yachts; Richard recognised the biggest, King George V's *Britannia* with her black hull, and also Sir Thomas Lipton's green *Shamrock V*, the white-jerseyed crew lying on deck like canned sardines in a long, neat row.

Shamrock sailed inshore and soon her canvas towered over them. Richard knew then the tremendous speed of the big yachts, which looked so slow from a distance, as *Shamrock* clove her way through the water close at hand. An order was called out and the white-clad crew rose at once and went to their stations to tend the sheets. Twenty men heaved in unsion on the mainsheet alone, one of the sails rattled like a machine-gun until it was properly trimmed, and *Shamrock* headed away towards Cawsand Bay, the half-roar, half-hiss waterfall noise of her passage diminishing. And there was Richard, not merely one of the thousands of spectators blackening the Hoe and foreshore, but actually sailing the same water as the great yachts. It was worth all the bother and anxiety of getting there — even worth being shouted at by Commander Jones.

That night, by the time he'd climbed home to Lower Port View, Richard had a new ambition: to sail in a race. With luck, he could start with the sailing club across the river at St.

Budeaux, which held races on Wednesday evenings and Saturday afternoons all the summer. Perhaps some boat owner would need an experienced foresheethand like himself.

Twice a week Richard put on his white jersey and plimsolls, crossed in the Saltash ferry and hovered around the foreshore on the St. Budeaux side, where most of the racing boats were kept. Others came from the Lynher River and only one from Saltash, where she was moored off the wharf. All boats seemed to have a regular crew of two or three, and Richard could only watch from the shore with the old men who knew all about sailing and could tell you what the helmsmen were doing wrong.

One helmsman they didn't criticise: Roy from the Lynher. Whatever Roy did was bound to be right. He was not always the first to finish, because he was up against faster boats, but Roy was the acknowledged expert, who understood the way of a sailing boat in the midst of the river, among the tides and eddies, the wind-flukes and the squalls.

The sailing committee, who attended the start and finish line at St. Budeaux wharf, and fired guns and flew signal flags, also administered a handicap system which altered from race to race, allowing time to all except the 'scratch' boat, which was Roy's *Maggie Dee*. After each race, the result was posted on a board, showing how the boats were placed after time allowance, and what the handicap would be for the next race, after adjustment to penalise the more successful boats. Richard followed every detail, and yearned to belong to one of the boats; he would have been proud to crew even the slowest.

One Saturday afternoon late in the season, *Maggie Dee* appeared off Henn Point on her way to the starting line. As she approached the wharf, Richard could see Roy at the helm, and he was alone. Roy spilt the wind and came gently alongside the ladder with the sails flogging. He looked up and called out, "Anyone like a sail?"

Richard held up his hand.

"Come on, then," said Roy, beckoning.

Richard was down the ladder in a moment, and standing on *Maggie Dee's* floorboards, unable to believe his luck.

"Ever sailed before?" asked Roy, pushing the boat off the wall.

"I sailed with Commander Jones once," boasted Richard.

Roy threw back his head and laughed. "All right, we'll start from the beginning."

As the sails drew, Richard found himself sitting with the correct foresheet in his hand, listening to Roy's quiet explanation of his duties, the boat heading out into the river. They practised tacking and gybing twice, Richard handling the foresheets and the plate (as Roy called the centreboard). The boat was very light and quick to respond to the trim of the sails and the weight of the crew; otherwise she handled something like Commander Jones' boat, but without the shouting.

A gun fired on shore.

"Five minutes," said Roy, looking at his wristwatch.

Then followed a hectic period, manoeuvring close to the other boats. Roy calling out, "Ease sheets . . . Haul the wind again . . . Ready about . . . Lee-o . . . Ease sheets . . . No, leave the plate where it is until I tell you . . . Now sheet her in . . ." then yelling at another boat, "Starboard!" to establish his right of way, and somehow avoiding a certain collision.

Richard's mouth ran dry, and the excitement of the start reached from his hair to his toes.

"Twenty-five seconds," said Roy. "We're going for the line. Get the rest of the plate down . . . Starboard!"

The gun fired again and *Maggie Dee* crossed the starting line ahead of the others, but Roy muttered, "Four seconds late . . . Ready about . . . Lee-o."

They tacked towards the Cornish side and Richard asked, "Why are we going over here?"

"Better tide . . . Sheet her in, harder."

With the rest of the fleet trailing them, Richard wouldn't have changed places with anyone in the world. This was his first sailing race, and he was in the leading boat already, sitting out alongside the best of helmsmen. They tacked twice more and reached the 'weather mark,' as Roy called it, with a good lead.

"Ease sheets," said Roy, "And get three quarters of the plate up."

They sailed up-river now, towards the next mark off Coombe Creek. Roy steered for the shore instead of straight for the mark, and grinned at Richard's puzzled look.

"You see that line of flotsam?" he explained. "That marks the edge of the main tide against us; the shore side of it we'll be in the eddy. But too close ashore we lose the wind. After the Coombe mark, we'll have the wind just about dead astern, and I'll want you to boom out the foresail, opposite side to the mainsail. You use that spar there, look. One end fits in an eye on the mast, just above the main boom fitting. Got it? The other end fits in the clew of the foresail — where the sheets are fastened. See the thimble in the corner? Have a look at the spar and you can see which end is which."

Richard looked as he was told and it seemed simple enough He was desperately anxious not to make any mistake, but though he'd never boomed out a foresail before, he didn't see how the operation could possibly go wrong.

But it did! At the mark, Roy steered to bring the wind astern and the foresail filled on the port side. Richard sheeted it correctly and just when he'd fitted the little boom, the wind caught the foresail aback momentarily and then filled it again with a whipcrack. The boom jumped out of the mast fitting, dropped out of the clew, bounced on the gunwhale and went overboard. Like lightning, Richard let go the foresheet and grabbed overboard with both hands, to save the foresail boom. He reached it, with his foot safely under the toe-strap, but when he came to heave himself back into the boat, he couldn't. He'd rolled the whole boat onto her side and she kept rolling, the water pouring into her. *Maggie Dee* settled on her side and stayed there.

In three seconds Richard had blown the race. He found himself swimming, still grasping the little spar. The chill of immersion in salt water was nothing compared to the sense of shame in the pit of his stomach. He looked at Roy, who was hanging grimly to the stern of the boat, his head and shoulders still dry.

"Gosh!" gasped Richard. "Sorry!"

"G-got to get the sails off her," said Roy, his teeth

chattering, "before we try to right her. You'll have to do it. I c—can't swim."

Under Roy's direction, Richard lowered the sails, if 'lower' is the right word when the sails are floating horizontally. Standing on the plate, Richard next pulled *Maggie Dee* upright, and clambered in over the bow. A motor-boat which was standing by lent them a bucket to bale with and Richard had to work like a Trojan to gain on the water coming up through the centreboard case, even after he'd plugged the slot with the foresail. But he won the battle and got *Maggie Dee* floating high again.

In due course Roy wriggled aboard over the stern and took over bailing. Richard was exhausted. The race was over by this time.

Roy set sail and landed a crestfallen Richard at Saltash jetty, refusing his offer of help in sailing *Maggie Dee* back to her berth on the Lynher.

"No, you go and get dry clothes on," said Roy. "So long."

Richard trudged up the jetty steps and stood watching *Maggie Dee* and the famous Roy sail away. He felt knee-high to a worm. Heaven had sent him the most wonderful opportunity, and he's thrown it overboard. There was a lump of lead where his stomach should have been.

Presently he saw Roy head back to the jetty, handing foresheets, mainsheet, tiller and plate like two men.

"Hey!" Roy yelled up to Richard. "You all right for Wednesay? . . . Six o'clock? . . . Here? . . . Don't you be late!"

SAINT MATTHEW FAIR

FRED'S folks didn't like him going out with Alice. His father used to say, "You'd do better to keep up your boxing, and leave the girls alone for a year or two."

But that wasn't why Fred had to do the milking on the Friday of Saint Matthew Fair; it was just his turn. Friday was the big day, when the fat bullocks went through the ring, and there was some up-country money about.

Fred brought the cows in early, and skimped the record-keeping, but it was still nearly seven o'clock before he was changed and on the road with his motor-bike.

As arranged, he called on Alice. She wasn't pleased about the late start, and grumbled, "It's hardly worth going. I can't stay out late, anyway, what with Mother being poorly."

"Oh, come on, Alice," said Fred. "There's still time to have some fun."

Then she saw the motor-bike, instead of the car she'd been expecting.

"Fred!" she squealed. "You know I hate motor-cycles."

"Well," he explained, "at least we'll get right into town, instead of parking outside, and having to walk the rest of the way."

Fred took the journey slowly, not to frighten Alice, but she looked white and shaken when they arrived. He parked the bike in the Square, and Alice recovered after some drinks at Webb's which knocked a big hole in Fred's spending money.

They got to the fairground at last, and Alice demanded the biggest woolly toy rabbit at the shooting gallery. Fred was nearly broke before he'd scored enough for that rabbit, and Alice didn't say 'Thank you' either.

"I thought you were supposed to be a good shot," she taunted him.

The cocoa-nut shy was the last straw. Even a direct hit, hard enough to smash the wooden throwing-ball, didn't shift its cocoa-nut, and all Fred got was a shout of laughter from Ralph, who turned up with Alice's sister.

"Here, Alice," he said. "You'll be here all night. Have one of ours."

Alice fawned on him as he handed her a cocoa-nut. Of course, Fred had to carry the thing, and look forward to spending the rest of the evening with an empty pocket, a sour Alice and a hairy great cocoa-nut.

Presently Ralph called out, "Look! The boxing booth. Come on, let's see what's happening."

Stripped to the waist, three silent, well-made chaps stood on a stage under a floodlight. With arms folded, and blank expression, they looked the very picture of sleeping tigers. They were joined by a fourth man, in white singlet and trousers, who raised a loud-hailer to his face and commenced his spiel.

"Ro-oll hup! Ro-oll hup! Welcome to the Southern Counties Boxing Academy! Come and see the noble art of self-defence, practised in style and beauty! Ro-oll hup! Ro-oll hup! Hevery contest in the Southern Counties Boxing Academy is a genuine contest, and hevery challenger is a genuine challenger! I'll give one hundred pounds to any charity you nominate if you can prove me wrong! Ro-oll hup! Ro-oll hup for the finest entertainment you've seen since the Southern Counties Boxing Academy was in Liskeard last year! Weight for weight, my boys bar none; I don't say they're world-beaters, but they're tough, they're experienced and they know their trade. And here's five pounds waiting" (the spieler flourished a bundle of bank-notes) "for any challenger who can beat my boy, weight for weight! But no weaklings, please. No dilly-tanties. An honest challenger, please, who knows how to look after himself. A man who can stand toe to toe and punch it out . . ."

Standing a little in front of him in the crowd Fred saw Vic Stevens, who'd been a top-notch amateur a few years before;

he'd trained Fred at the boxing club until Alice had persuaded him to give it up a few months earlier. Fred thrust the cocoa-nut in Alice's hand and moved towards Vic, just as the spieler threw out his challenge, "Are there any men in Liskeard?"

The crowd stood motionless. Fred touched Vic on the shoulder and whispered, "Can I count on you in my corner?"

Vic recognised him, grinned and nodded.

The spieler taunted, "Do you breed men in Liskeard?"

That was enough. Fred pushed his way to the front and jumped into the stage.

"Middleweight," he announced himself.

A thin cheer arose from the crowd and a buzz of excited conversation, and someone yelled, "Good old Fred! Show him, Fred!" which was the signal for a louder cheer.

"What's your name, mate?" asked the spieler, who was a sharp-looking customer when you got close to him.

"Fred Hooper."

"And who are you?" the spieler challenged Vic.

"I'm looking after Fred," explained Vic. "I do it in all his fights. That your middleweight?" Vic nodded towards a stocky character wearing green silk trunks and bearing the marks of heavy punishment on his face.

"That's my boy," confirmed the spieler and, raising his loud-hailer again, he announced, "We have a challenger! Ladies and gentlemen, we have a challenger from Liskeard! He doesn't know what he's taken on yet, but he'll get a fair fight in the Southern Counties Boxing Academy. Your own Fred Hooper has challenged Billy Barnwell, who has fought and beaten some of the best welterweights and middleweights in the British Isles!" (The spieler paused for the applause to subside.) "It will be a great contest, gentlemen! The price to suit our pockets is only one shilling, and the ladies are specially invited . . ."

Invited or not, Alice had worked her way up to the front of the stage, still clutching the enormous toy rabbit and the cocoa-nut, and she was gazing up at Fred with her mouth open.

He dropped on one knee and told her, "Don't worry, Alice. We could do with that five pounds."

To tell the truth, he'd started to do a little worrying on his own account. No-one knew better than he did that the five pounds weren't in the bag yet by a long way.

Vic took him by the elbow and said, "Come on, Fred. Better get changed and gloved up. The cash customers are rolling in."

Behind the tent was a motor caravan, the interior of which stank of fried fish and stale sweat. In charge of the caravan was an ageing, punch-drunk gnome who'd no doubt in his day fought and beaten some of the best flyweights in the British Isles. His eyes, nose, mouth and even his ears constantly twitched, and the twitching killed any expression his face might otherwise have shown.

"Is this where we change?" asked Vic.

"That's right ... Who's the ... challenger?" asked the gnome, between twitches. "He can use ... any of that gear ... over there."

Vic selected two pairs of boxing boots for Fred's approval, and a pair of black trunks with red trimmings. Fred slipped off his clothes and put them in a neat bundle on a shabby settee.

Billy Barnwell was already in the ring when Fred arrived. He was sitting calmly on a stool, his head covered by a towel. The spieler was also in the ring, surveying the crowd from a neutral corner.

Fred climbed up and ducked through the ropes into the heat and glare of the floodlights. Then he found he had strong support at the ringside, and it put fresh heart in him. But the waiting was agony.

At last, when the tent was crammed full of spectators, the spieler stepped into the middle of the ring. He raised his arms and announced, "Laid-ees and gentlemen, this ... is a middleweight contest of three rounds, three minutes each round, between — and introducing to you — the Iron Man, Billy Barnwell of Liverpool" (half-hearted applause, while Billy rose, whipped the towel from his head and bowed briskly to the four corners of the tent) "and the challenger, Fred Hooper of Lisk . . ."

A roar from the crowd drowned the spieler's bellow, and it surprised Fred. He didn't know he had so many friends, but felt he needed every one of them. There might, after all, be something in the power of prayer.

While the spieler completed the announcement about the referee (himself) and the timekeeper (the twitching gnome), Vic gripped the towel around Fred's shoulders and lectured him urgently.

"Box clever, Fred. No point in mixing it with this bloke, not until you know more about him. You've got the reach. Keep him off. You've got a good left hand. Make it work for you. And keep moving. Move all the time. Don't stand still, for heaven's sake! There you go . . ."

Spieler called them into the middle. Billy looked weary. Spieler spoke confidentially to both of them, but his remarks were meant for Fred.

"Let's have a good hard scrap. Plenty of action. These good people have paid hard-earned money to watch you blokes. Give 'em value, and I'll let the loser take the hat round afterwards. You'll do all right."

Raising his voice, Spieler added, "Shake hands now, go back to your corners, and when the bell goes, come out fighting."

Vic had just time to remind Fred to keep moving and keep his left working, when the bell clanged and Fred was facing Billy across the gloves. Being the shorter man, Billy had to get inside Fred's reach, and he came in. Fred gave ground until he felt the ropes against his back. He sidestepped as Billy jumped in. When Billy stumbled, Fred rammed a good hard left in his face, which brought a shout from the crowd. When he tried another, Billy slipped inside and got a couple of digs in his ribs before Fred smothered him.

"Break!" yelled Spieler and they broke clean. Fred felt more relaxed now. Billy cut out most of the work and he had the better of the infighting when Fred wasn't smart enough to avoid it; he had to take some stick from Fred's left hand, though, before he could get close enough to score.

Towards the end of the first round, Fred was confident enough to stand square and swap punches with him until Billy broke off the engagement. The crowd went wild with excitement, and the boxers didn't hear the bell for the end of the round, so Spieler had to separate them and send them back to their corners.

If Fred thought Vic would be pleased with his performance, he had a rude awakening.

"You do that once more, and you'll be back in this corner like a sack of potatoes! You fight your way, not his. I'm disappointed in you, Fred. You did all right till you got cocky. Start brawling with Billy over there and he'll carve you up. You're here to win five pounds, not to show off to your girl-friend."

"Is Alice in here?" asked Fred, peering round the ringside.

"Shut up!" snapped Vic. "Breathe deep and listen."

Vic lectured him so sternly on the classic boxing virtues, that when the bell went for the second round, Fred was bewildered as he got to his feet. Billy was almost in his corner. Fred moved out as Billy caught him with his right, too high on the head to do much damage, but Fred knew he'd been hit. He had just wits enough to hold Billy off with a one-two as he tried to follow up.

Then the bout settled down to the pattern of Fred boxing clever and Billy trying all he knew to land his right again. He let it go several times and the draught from it made Fred's hair stand on end. Now and again Fred's left glove connected with Billy's face, especially after Billy'd missed with a block-buster, and each time the crowd shouted with joy. When the second round ended, Fred felt on top of the world, though he was breathing hard, due to his lack of training.

Vic was better pleased, but he continued the lecture where he'd left off.

"You're ahead now, Fred, but Billy isn't going to let you get away with it easily. You've still got to work for that fiver.

You've got three mintues left, to stay out of trouble. Keep moving all the time. Move to your right, away from his right. Keep your left working all the time. And don't get cornered, if you can help it. If you do, jump in and hold. Don't worry about the referee; just look after yourself."

Fred and Billy touched gloves at the start of the last round, but when Fred stepped back politely, Billy didn't. Before Fred knew what was happening, he was bundled into a corner on the receiving end of some hard digs. The crowd noise was tremendous.

Then Fred was sitting on the floor in the corner and Spieler was counting over him, shouting above the crowd, "...three...four..."

Fred's head cleared and he distinctly heard Vic say, "When you get up, go to the middle and get your left going."

"... seven... eight..." continued Spieler.

Fred moved into the middle while in the act of rising. Billy was surprised, but he was soon on the attack again, to follow up his advantage. Fred sidestepped the first rush, to the huge delight of the crowd, and even planted a weak left in Billy's face while he was off balance. But from now on it was hard work, and Fred collected some nasty digs as the round wore on. Several times he held Billy's arms, and got told off by Spieler. Also, Billy butted him in the eye during one of these clinches.

When they broke that time, Billy had blood on his face. Fred didn't know until afterwards that it wasn't Billy's blood.

Presently he heard Vic shout, "Half a minute left, Fred."

This time when Billy came in, Fred met him with a right which stopped him in his tracks. He got in another left and right before Billy could get himself working again, and the crowd loved it.

From then until the bell, they threw in everything, though Fred hadn't much left to throw. The cheering went on fully half a minute after the bell. Billy bared his gum-shield at Fred in a grin and patted his head patronisingly before returning to his stool and covering his head with his towel.

Vic sponged Fred's face and said, "There wasn't much in it. I reckon he did just enough to win. The crowd won't like it, though, that was the dirtiest handshake I ever saw at the start of the last. And your eye looks bad; he did that with his head."

Through the other eye, Fred saw Spieler raise his arms for silence and announce, "Lai-dees and gentlemen, I'm sure you would want me to congratulate both boxers on a splendid contest." (Hesitant applause.) "The winner is Barnwell."

There followed a deafening howl of protest, which settled into a prolonged Boo-oo-oo-oo.

Fists were shaken and threats hurled at Spieler and it was a full minute before that thick-skinned character could continue his announcement. By that time, Fred was leaving the ring.

"Gentlemen, please... I'm sure you want to show your appreciation of a very gallant challenger." (Renewed cheering.) "It is the right of hevery challenger in the South Counties Boxing Academy to pass the hat round when he's put up a good performance, so give generously, gentlemen, to a fellow-sportsman... And now for your further entertainment, an exhibition bout of three rounds, two minutes each round, between — and introducing to you ..."

The gnome accosted Fred at the ringside and thrust a cloth cap into his still-gloved hands.

"Remember," he twitched confidentially, "you split it... fifty-fifty."

Vic reminded Fred, "You've lost your amateur status, anyway, so you might as well get what you can out of it."

A half-crown fell into the cap, followed by another, and another. Fred moved around slowly, collecting the nobbins. Vic stayed at his side, confiding in the patrons and loosening their purse-strings.

"We've got another Len Harvey here... A little more experience and he could go right to the top ... What do you say, do we breed men in Liskeard?"

It was Hosken the butcher who dropped the first pound note in the cap; several more followed. The Member of Parliament (Conservative, of course) stumped up a five-pound note and drawled, "Vert gutty show, Hooper. Well done!"

As soon as he could, Fred told Vic, "Whip that fiver, quick. We're not going to split that with the plug-uglies."

Alice forgot all about going home early. She clung possessively to Fred's arm all evening, and they had the freedom of Liskeard. They weren't allowed to buy a drink or even a hot-dog, nor were they kept waiting for anything. Friends slapped Fred's back and complete strangers wrung his hand.

About eleven o'clock, Fred had had enough unaccustomed glory, and he decided to take Alice home. She mounted the pillion without a murmur.

At her father's farm, she persuaded Fred to leave the bike at the road-gate, and walk her down to the yard. There she pacified the growling watch-dog and suggested, "We can say 'Goodnight' in the hay-loft. Mother's gone to bed, so there's no hurry."

Women are funny creatures ..

HARVEST TIME AT PENCRINNICK

AUNTIE Florence wasn't really George's aunt; she was his mother's cousin. George called her Auntie Florence because she was grown-up.

Auntie Florence had recently married a farmer, and as there'd been no farmer in the family since Great-grandpa, it was a change for George to spend the summer holidays on a farm. Auntie Florence's and Uncle Colin's farm was called Pencrinnick.

The exciting thing about Pencrinnick was all the young animals and birds. Besides a couple of new-born calves, there was a litter of piglets, lots of growing-up calves and lambs, kittens of all colours and several broods of chicks. What with all these, the wildlife, the corn getting bigger every day and the hay "aiming up for a second cut," as Uncle Colin said, Pencrinnick was bursting with life and growth.

Auntie Florence ran the dairy. The milk was brought up to her in the morning and evening, and she made cream with the new Alfa-Laval separator. George's mother said it didn't look like what she called cream, but Auntie Florence said you could sell it as cream and that was all that mattered to her.

One day at dinner, which Auntie Florence served at lunch-time, Uncle Colin said he was going to make room for the first-calvers by culling three or four old cows. "They've been here long enough," he said.

"What do you mean, culling, Uncle Colin?" asked George.

"Getting rid of them," he replied.

"Where will they go?"

"The butchers," explained Uncle Colin, casually.

The awful prospect took George's appetite away. Uncle Colin could keep a cow for ages, take care of her and her calves, get all that milk out of her, and then go and sell the cow for meat just because she was getting old.

It seemed to George that the innocent creatures were the ones who suffered: the long-serving cows, the half-grown pigs who went for bacon, and the chicks who were always having accidents, so that the broods got smaller almost every day. Nothing ever happened to nasty, aggressive animals like Wesley's ferrets. Wesley was the son of one of Uncle Colin's men, and he laughed when his dog ferret bit George's thumb. George's mother said people got to be like their animals, but perhaps it was the other way round in Wesley's case.

If Pencrinnick teemed with life, there was violent death, too, and both were taken for granted. One day Uncle Colin walked into the kitchen carrying a chicken by the feet with its head cut off and its wings still flapping; all Auntie Florence was concerned about was the blood dripping all over her clean kitchen flagstones. It wasn't a bit like being home in Truro, where George was forbidden to go anywhere near the slaughterhouse, and the subject of death was carefully avoided.

Uncle Colin's men were strange, too. George couldn't understand their talk; perhaps they spoke the old Cornish language. Anyway, you wouldn't hear anything like it in Truro. Nor would you see men work like they did. Hours on end they worked, like the horses they looked after, without ever tiring. George wasn't allowed to work with them on the second hay harvest, because he would only get in the way.

Another thing you didn't get in the city was the farm smells: the new hay drying out in the rick; the linseedy smell of the cattle-cake Uncle Colin bought for the winter, and the fresh cow-dung in the yard where the cows waited patiently to be milked. For years afterwards, these smells reminded George of Pencrinnick.

One evening after studying the sky, Uncle Colin declared that the corn harvest would start next day. Even George would be allowed to help.

The corn was cut by a reaping-and-binding machine which everyone called the 'binder,' drawn by the two strongest horses. Long knives on spokes revolved at the side of the binder, like the great wheel of a paddle steamer, and the standing corn disappeared into the machine, but only for a few seconds until it slid off the back, tied in sheaves.

George's job was to gather the sheaves and stack them in shocks of ten or twelve, propping each other up with the grain on top. The womenfolk, including George's mother and

Auntie Florence part of the time, also did this job. Wesley was supposed to do it, too, but he sulked because he couldn't have a pitchfork and work with the men like his elder brother.

A wagon with Uncle Colin's other two horses came round to collect each shock, taking full loads down to the corner of ten-acre. A huge rick base was laid out there, and George was proud to be helping in such an enormous task.

Everyone had pasty lunch together at the new rick, as there wasn't time to go indoors. The men drank cider, but George and Wesley had tea with the women. Then the sheaf-gathering continued until the evening, when the binder and the wagon were unhitched and work was called off for the day. As a special treat, George was lifted on to the withers of Prince, one of the horses, and he rode back to the yard, clinging to the great leather collar.

Prince stopped at the yard pond and put his head down for a drink. The collar slipped down with George behind it. The collar stopped at Prince's head, but George went on, splashing into the muddy, shallow water. The worst thing about it was that Wesley saw it happen, and wouldn't stop laughing at George.

Pencrinnick had several cornfields and after two or three days of harvesting, the threshing machine arrived, drawn by a chugging steam tractor with even more polished brass on it than the horses had on their harness. The threshing machine was set up by the towering new rick in ten-acre, and you could hear it roaring while you were working two fields away.

Now the men built a second rick, while the first one was fed into the thresher. By dinner the following day, all the smaller cornfields had been cut and carried, and half of ten-acre remained. It became a race to complete the second rick before the thresher could swallow up the big one. Some of the men had to deal with the great pile of straw blown out by the thresher, stacking it in a tight, permanent rick; this was the most skilled job of all.

No men could be spared for the wagon now, so the remaining sheaves had to be carried by hand down to the bottom of the field. George was allowed no time to stand and watch the great, panting engine, or the steady stream of grain pouring out of the thresher into sacks.

When there was only a narrow patch of corn left standing in the centre of ten-acre, the men dropped their pitchforks and three of them, including Uncle Colin, fetched the guns they'd left under their coats by the hedge. The dogs jumped up, excited at the prospect of game. Everyone went towards the middle of the field, the guns leading and Uncle Colin growling at the dogs to keep them at heel.

George's mother called him away, so he wasn't very close when the dogs yelped, the men shouted and the guns banged. But he did see some rabbits darting out of the corn, and one of the dogs giving chase. With his eyes on a running rabbit, the dog ran straight into the binder. George heard him scream as the revolving knives caught him, and saw him trying to run afterwards on the stumps of his legs.

Transfixed with horror, George stood crying, "No! No! No!" as the nearest gun went to the stricken dog and shot him in the head.

George's mother tried to explain it as just an accident, but George thought things could never be the same again. He helped to carry the last sheaves, though his legs were like lead. The steam engine throbbed, the thresher roared and the men were soon laughing and joking, just as if nothing had happened. They were all like Wesley at Pencrinnick: nasty, unfeeling and violent.

That night when he said his prayers, George asked to go back to Truro, where he could get out his toy farm things on the attic floor again, and play farms in peace.

FATHER'S NAPOLEON BRANDY

"THOU shalt not steal."

Parson Traherne can never read this commandment, or repeat it to his congregation, without a pang of remorse. His guilt dates from his undergraduate days, just before he decided to read for holy orders.

It was his father's, Colonel Traherne's, Napoleon brandy that tempted him. There were two whole bottles of it — the colonel's pride and joy.

For many years, his father didn't even see the Napoleon brandy; it stood in its own little niche in the cellar, collecting frass and cobwebs. Norman Traherne didn't suppose his father would ever consider any celebration important enough to justify broaching it, and no-one would ever know if the bottles contained brandy, light ale or cold tea.

During his first long vacation from Oxford, Norman accepted a friend's invitation for the week-end. The friend's family was entertaining some Americans, and the intention was that his friend and he would accompany two American girls to the Tidworth Tattoo. Before Norman left for this week-end, he thought hard about the contribution he could make to the entertainment; he didn't like to join the party empty-handed.

He thought of the Napoleon brandy. He shrank at first from the idea of stealing it. But the more Norman thought about it, the more attracted he was by the prospect of offering a swig of the rare liquor to the American girls. Pocketing his silver hip-flask, a torch, a corkscrew and a small funnel, he went surreptitiously to the cellar.

He trembled with an excitement not all due to the fear of discovery: he was too exhilarated for that. Norman felt the fascination of crime: the Devil in him, perhaps.

He picked at one of the wax seals, carefully saving each flake; then he drilled the cork and drew it. Decanting some of the liquid into his flask, Norman sipped it and found it smooth as silk. He filled the flask to the neck, spilling some of the precious contents.

Old brandy bottles being small, he must have half emptied this one. Resolving to return and conceal the evidence of his theft later, Norman replaced the lightly-corked bottle and the pieces of wax on the niche ledge. Then he stealthily climbed the cellar steps with his flask full of his father's Napoleon brandy.

"It was sensational," said Norman's new friend, Eleanor, after the tattoo.

Eleanor was shivering, though, by the time they got back to the car, so Norman pulled out his hip-flask and poured a tot into its silver cap.

"This will warm you," he predicted.

"Say, what is that?" asked Eleanor suspiciously, remembering her strict New England upbringing.

"Brandy," replied Norman airily. "Napoleon brandy. It's well over a hundred years old."

"Gee, oh my!" squealed Eleanor. "More than a hundred years old!"

Eleanor drank, and so did her sister. They all had a tot, preparatory to dashing through the night air at fifty miles an hour in a MG sports car — a most fashionable pastime for an undergraduate on those days.

Snuggling close against Norman with her head on his shoulder, Eleanor confided, "I feel warm, right down to my toes."

On the journey, he caught the bouquet of Napoleon brandy in her breath from time to time.

Norman's pleasure evaporated when he returned home with the empty hip-flask. Only his guilt remained.

He sneaked down to the cellar with the means to cover his crime. He topped the brandy bottle up with water and forced the cork back, though he had to nick it with a razor-blade first. Last came the fiddling task of gluing the fragments of sealing-wax in place under torch-light. The whole operation occupied two hours, which seemed like a prolonged sentence in purgatory.

When he'd finished, Norman knew which bottle he'd tampered with, but he hoped no-one else would. He crept up the steps, praying that he wouldn't be seen emerging from the cellar door. His luck held.

As the weeks went by, Norman's anxiety receded. There were times when he wanted to go to his father and make a clean breast of it. Then he would think it kinder to spare the colonel the knowledge that his younger son was a sneak-thief.

Before the long vacation was over, Colonel Traherne entertained an old friend to lunch. The preparations occupied several days.

The day before the visitation, the colonel announced, "I think I'll open a bottle of the Napoleon brandy tomorrow, if one of you would be kind enough to bring it up."

Breathless, Norman squeaked, "I'll get it."

Pushing past his brother, he collected the torch from the hall and made his way down to the cellar. He shone the torch first on one seal and then the other, gripping each bottle in turn for fear of dropping it in his agitation. To his unspeakable dismay, Norman couldn't be sure which bottle he'd adulterated.

"Norman!" It was his brother's voice from the top of the cellar stairs, and Norman nearly jumped out of his skin.

He took a deep breath before answering, "Yes?"

"Father says please bring up a bottle of Latour for dinner."

"Right."

Thoroughly shaken and confused, Norman thought he could, after all, distinguish between the Napoleon bottles. Composing himself as best he could, he returned upstairs with one Napoleon brandy and one Chateau Latour.

Norman and his brother didn't meet the guest, because they drove to Redruth to watch a rugby match. Their father was not pleased with them.

On the way to the match, a thought struck Norman like a blow in the stomach: he had in his confusion extracted the adulterated bottle of brandy from the cellar, leaving the good one on the shelf. Could he have been such a fool? The more he thought about it, the more convinced he became that he'd brought the wrong bottle up to the light of day.

His brother glanced at him and asked, "Are you all right? You look as if you've seen a ghost."

Norman felt miserable all day, and desperately anxious on the return journey.

When they got home, their father was quiet and thoughtful. Neither he nor their mother mentioned brandy, and Norman dared not raise the subject. From that day to this, he hasn't discovered if the brandy was consumed or thrown out.

When the colonel died, the bulk of his estate passed to his wife for her lifetime. There were also some legacies. He left Norman his stock of wines. Norman was convinced that it was a reproach from beyond the grave.

He was married by that time, but he didn't even mention to his wife the last bottle of Napoleon brandy. At the first secret opportunity, he opened it, praying that the cork would prove to be the one he'd mutilated, and his father had enjoyed the unadulterated brandy.

The cork was absolutely sound. In his desolation, Norman poured the Napoleon brandy down the kitchen sink, and threw the empty bottle in the dustbin.